ENCHANTING INDIAN TALES
Megha and the Magic Tree

Harsha V. Dehejia

An imprint of Om Books International

Published in 2012 by

An imprint of Om Books International

Corporate & Editorial Office
A-12, Sector 64, Noida 201 301
Uttar Pradesh, India
Phone: +91 120 477 4100
Email: editorial@ombooks.com
Website: www.ombooksinternational.com

Sales Office
4379/4B, Prakash House, Ansari Road
Darya Ganj, New Delhi 110 002, India
Phone: +91 11 2326 3363, 2326 5303
Fax: +91 11 2327 8091
Email: sales@ombooks.com
Website: www.ombooks.com

ISBN: 978-93-81607-34-3

Printed in India

10 9 8 7 6 5 4 3 21

Black ink drawing by Badri Narayan

CREDITS

Art Consultant
Varsha Mehta

Design and Layout
Ratnakar Singh
Ryan Krieg

Artists
C.M. Bhandari
Prakash Israni
Uma Krishnaswamy
Asma Menon
Badri Narayan
Girish Patel
Parakshit Sharma
Trilok Soni
Leen Thobias
Rajesh Vora

Editor
Sonalini Chaudhry

The tree for us in India is an icon and a shrine.
It is a Kalpavriksha which grants
wishes and fulfils desires.
It is under the Kadamba tree
that we hear the flute of Krishna;
And under the Bodhi tree that we venerate the Buddha.
It is to the Vatavriksha that we tie threads;
And it is under the Parijataka tree
that we gather our puja flowers.
It is under a tree that rishis meditate and people rest.
When the wind blows through the Pipal tree,
we hear the hymns of the Vedas;
And it is under the tree that we
gather to listen to stories.
So come and listen to this story of
Megha and the Magic Tree.

MEGHA AND NANI
THE STORY OF THE FIRST MAGIC TREE

MEGHA was a sweet and playful girl with a beautiful face and every time she smiled, there would be a dimple on her cheek. Nine-year-old Megha was dressed in a traditional Indian dress of chania-choli, skirt and blouse, and a matching scarf called odhni. And her hair was tied neatly in two pig tails. Megha had no brothers or sisters. She was good in her studies and worked very hard to please her teacher. She always did her homework on time and never got into any trouble at school. She liked all her classmates but was not very friendly with them. During the school recess, she would finish her lunch and read from a book that she would bring from home rather than play with the other children. Her mother would drop her to school in the morning but in the afternoon, she would walk to her Nani's house which was very near her own.

Little Megha in her chania-choli and odhni

She was not really her Nani but an old lady who had no family and she loved Megha. Nani would give her a glass of milk and biscuits and Megha would sit with her and talk to her. Nani would tell her different stories of gods and goddesses and kings and queens and Megha would sit by her knee and be spellbound by these stories. She heard stories of Krishna and of Shiva, of Savitri and Satyabhama and many more. Megha would ask Nani lots of questions, and Nani would answer her patiently. But sometimes when she did not have an answer, she would laugh and put her hand on Megha's head and say that when she grew up, she would find out the answers for herself. Nani's face was wrinkled, her earlobes had large holes, her hair was white and she had no teeth. She was bent over with age and walked with a stick, but her eyes were radiant and in every wrinkle there were years of wisdom. Her hands were worn but agile and she would never let them be idle for she would sew, knit or crochet and make little things to give away to others, keeping nothing for herself.

Megha loved her a lot and Nani would always wait for Megha at the front door in the afternoon. Nani's home was simple and small, just one room with a bed and a rocking chair. Next to her bed was a rickety table on which she kept her glasses, a time piece and her prayer beads, the japa mala. On the wall across was a calendar with a picture of Krishna and the cows. She would sit in the rocking chair and cover her legs with a blanket as her feet would get cold. Nani could not walk

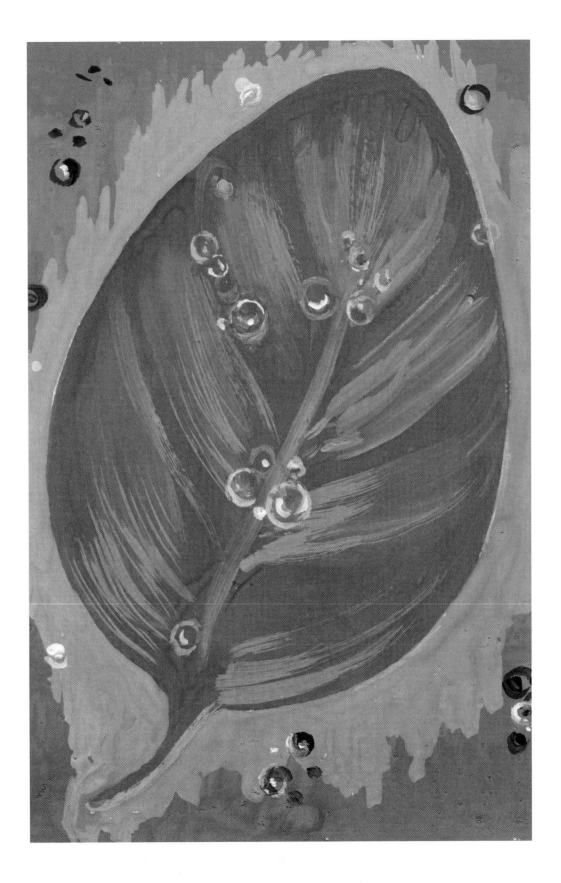

too much as her knees would hurt and Megha would rub some balm on them. Sometimes Nani would fall asleep even when she was talking. And when this happened, Megha would open her school bag and do her homework at the foot of the chair as she did not want to disturb Nani when she was asleep.

Megha would often bring something from her house for her Nani. Sometimes she would bring a flower from her garden, at other times she would ask her mother to give her a laddu, an Indian sweet. Last month on Purnima, the full moon night, there was a religious ceremony called Satyanarayan katha at her house. There was a lot of dried fruit in the prasad, the offering that was made to the gods. Megha saved her prasad and gave it to Nani. Once, when she saw that Nani's blanket was torn and worn, Megha asked her mother if she could take a rajai, a warm quilt, for her Nani. Megha and Nani were the best of friends and when Megha was not able to meet Nani, she would miss her a lot.

One day, when Megha arrived at Nani's house, she was not there. Megha looked everywhere and then found a note on the small table next to her bed. It said, "Megha, I have had to go to the doctor—I was not feeling too well. I will be late coming home. I have left some biscuits for you. Get home safe. I love you very much. Nani." When she read the note, Megha felt very worried about her Nani and could not sleep all night.

The next day, Megha could not pay attention to the teacher in school and the teacher even scolded her. As soon as school finished, she ran to her Nani's house. Nani was not standing at the door like she usually did, but was in bed, her eyes half closed. As soon as she entered, Megha began to cry. Nani raised her arms and gave Megha a big hug. "I am so glad to see you," Megha said. "Why did you have to go to the doctor yesterday?"

"I had a terrible pain in my chest and I could not breathe," Nani's voice was weak. Megha sat beside her on her bed and held her hand.

"I do not know whether I will see you again and I want to give you something. I do not have too many possessions, but many years ago a sadhu gave me a seed wrapped in a red cloth. I do not know what it is and I have preserved it under my pillow for all these years. I feel that it protects me and I want you to have it. Keep it safely with you and that way you and I will always be together." Nani reached under her pillow and gave Megha the strange seed and as she did, her hands shook and she fell asleep. Megha burst into tears and kept her head on Nani's chest and she could hear her breathing with great difficulty.

Megha left as it was getting very late—but before leaving, she ran back and touched Nani's feet and put her hand on her forehead. She felt blessed.

When Megha went home, she hid the seed between her clothes so that her mother would not see it. She quickly finished her homework and after eating dinner, went up to her room. She looked at the seed and held it to her chest. She wondered what that seed would do for her but since it was given by her Nani, she felt sure that it was very special and sacred. She clutched it in her hand and fell asleep.

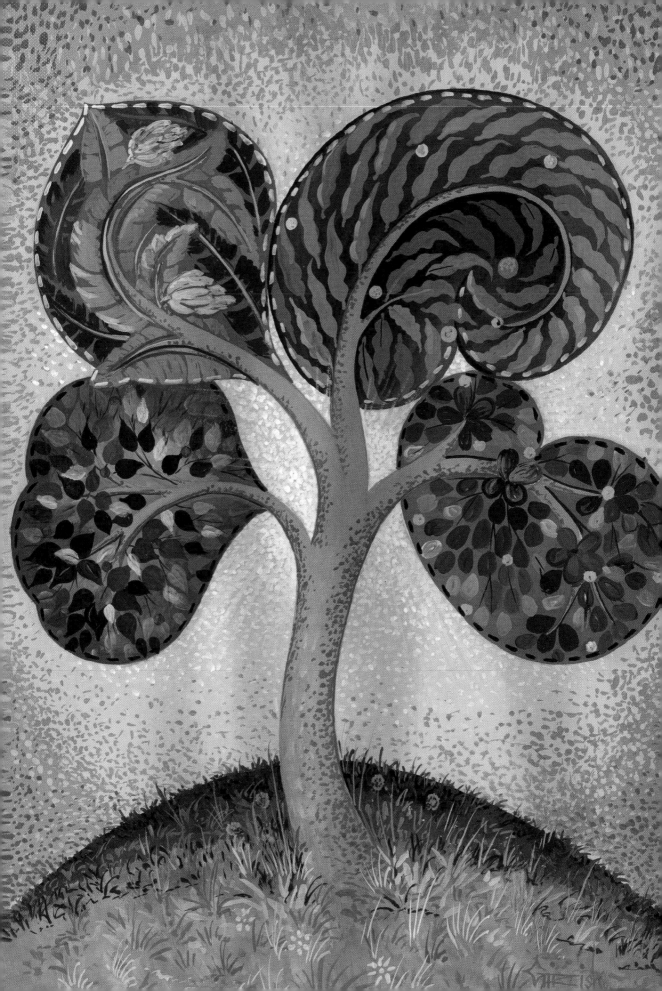

Megha got up in the middle of the night as she saw a bright glow in the garden. She went to the window of her room and saw a beautiful tree glowing in the garden. It was as if there were tiny lights on all its branches. It had four branches and each was different. One was the branch of a Kadamba tree, the other of a Banyan tree, the third of a Pipal tree and the fourth was that of an Ashoka tree.

Megha quietly went into the garden and stood beside the branch of the Kadamba. Soon there appeared many gopis, cowherd girls, dressed in attractive chania-cholis and odhnis just like her. They held hands and formed a circle. Soon there were other gopis with musical instruments—one with a drum called the dholak, another with hand cymbals called the manjira, and a third with an unique single-stringed instrument called the ektara. There was music all around, and then appeared Krishna, the flute-playing god. He was dressed in pitambar, yellow-coloured garments had a crown of peacock feathers and wore a vanmala, a garland of leaves and flowers.

Krishna went to the centre of the circle of gopis and started to play his flute. The gopis clapped their hands and went round and round in a circle around Krishna. The full moon of Sharada, the time for harvest, appeared in the sky. There flew Gandharvas in their celestial vehicles, showering flowers on the circle of gopis. Soon something magical happened—from a single Krishna in the middle of the circle there were many Krishnas, so that there was a Krishna between two gopis. Megha watched all this and felt very happy. She went to the garden and as she was standing there, Krishna went to her and drew her into the circle. Megha danced and clapped with all the other gopis all night. And as the full moon of Sharada was fading, Krishna told Megha, "Always keep your mind as sweet as the song of my flute."

Krishna and the gopis form a circle around Megha

When Megha got up in the morning, the dream of Krishna and the gopis stayed with her all day. And even when she was at school, she thought of the Rasa dance of Krishna and the gopis and the sound of the flute. She decided that she would keep her mind as sweet as the music of Krishna.

When school was over she went to Nani's house but the door was locked. She wondered where Nani had gone.

That night, thinking of her Nani, Megha slept with the seed in her hand. Again, she was awakened by a bright glow in the garden and she saw the same tree. This time, under the Pipal branch, she saw a young prince. He was very handsome and was riding a horse. His attendants shouted, "Hail Siddhartha, Prince of Lumbini!" The prince kept on riding and he came across four men. One was an old man, the second a sick man, the third a dead man and the fourth was a sadhu who looked very peaceful. Prince Siddhartha was disturbed by the four sights and wondered about the emptiness and fragility of life. He got down from the horse and discarded his royal clothes and wore a simple robe made of tattered fabrics. He sat under the Pipal tree. Cross legged, with his hands placed on each other and his eyes closed, he meditated and he looked very peaceful. Soon a lot of people had gathered around this meditating prince and they said, "This must be the Buddha, the Enlightened One." They chanted, "Buddham sharanam gacchami—I go to the Buddha for refuge." Buddha opened his eyes and blessed everyone; he even invited Megha to the Pipal tree under which he was sitting and told her, "Come, my child. Live a happy life but understand that the world is full of sadness. Even so, never forget that in spite of this, your mind is always blissful. If you live your life knowing this, you will never be unhappy."

She was spellbound by this and listened closely as the Buddha said, he told her, "Always be peaceful and never let anything take away the inner peace of your mind."

When Megha got up in the morning, she thought of Buddha all day and his message of peace resonated in her mind. She decided that she would always be peaceful and would love everyone.

Megha could not wait for the day to finish. She hurried through dinner and went to her room and fell asleep with the seed in her hand. Once again, in the middle of the night, a bright glow from the garden woke her up. She saw that the Banyan branch was shining like gold; underneath it there were many women who were tying threads around the Banyan tree and performing a puja. She stood there and asked one of the women what they were doing. They said that it was Vata Savitri day and they were performing a ritual so that their husbands would live long. "What is Vata Savitri?" Megha asked. One of the ladies sat with Megha under the Banyan tree and began telling her the story of Savitri.

Savitri was the beautiful daughter of a king and when she grew up, her father looked around in his kingdom for an appropriate young groom for her. Savitri told her father that she would marry a person of her choice and not that of her father's. One day, when she was wandering in the forest, she met a handsome young man called Satyavan and fell in love with him. He was a prince but lived in the forest as his father had lost his kingdom. Satyavan spent his time looking after his parents who had become blind. When Savitri announced to her father her intention to marry Satyavan, he was enraged. The

father called the court astrologer who predicted that Satyavan would die within a year. Savitri insisted that she would marry Satyavan and no other. The king had no choice but to give in. Savitri married Satyavan and the two of them lived in the forest, looking after Satyavan's aging parents. Exactly a year later, while they were in the forest, Satyavan complained that he was feeling very tired. Savitri asked him to rest his head in her lap and just then Yama, the God of Death appeared. He told Savitri that Satyavan's time on earth had come to an end and that he had come to take him. Savitri refused to part with Satyavan and told Yama that she would not be separated from her husband. Yama was touched by her devotion and told

Women tying threads around the Banyan tree and performing a puja

Savitri to ask him for a boon. Savitri said that she wanted to be the mother of eight children and that she and Satyavan should live long enough to serve their parents. Yama was pleased and restored Satyavan to life and the two of them lived happily ever after. The ladies who were tying threads around the Banyan tree held Megha's hand and told her that in life one should be fearless in love and use that love to serve humanity.

Megha woke up in the morning and the story of Savitri and Satyavan was on her mind all day. She rushed home after school and soon went to sleep, hoping that she would see another beautiful vision.

Once again, Megha awoke in the middle of the night because of a radiant glow from the garden. She got up and went down and saw that a beautiful woman was holding the branch of the Ashoka tree and with her left foot she was touching the trunk. As soon as the tree felt the touch of the woman, it burst into blossoms. Megha was spellbound and went to the woman and asked, "Who are you?" The woman said, "I am a Salabhanjika, the graceful feminine form, and I am recreating an ancient rite. In times ancient, I used to be a yakshi, a tree spirit, and lived in trees. Maya, Buddha's mother, passing through a Sal forest, developed labour pains. Holding on to the branch of the Sal tree, she gave birth to Siddhartha. From then on, young and beautiful women talk to trees and make them come alive; trees, in turn, long for the touch of women. The sap or rasa flowing in trees is no different from the rasa animating these women. Women and trees share their fertility and beauty."

Megha was captivated by this and asked, "May I touch the tree as well?"

"Of course, why not," said the Salabhanjika. "Instead of touching the tree, just breathe on it." Megha went near the tree and breathed on a branch. To her surprise, beautiful and perfumed red flowers appeared on the branch. The Salabhanjika taught Megha other rites like singing to the tree, dancing in front of the tree, filling the mouth with fragrant water and spraying the tree with it. Each time Megha did this, the tree would put out new and fragrant flowers which would sing. Megha was so touched by all this that she hugged the tree. As she did that, the tree shed its flowers and poured them on her head till her head was covered and she looked like a bride. The Salabhanjika sat Megha close to her and told her that trees were very special. She whispered in Megha's ear, "Vrikshah rakhshati rakshitah—let us protect trees that protect us." She also said that the association of the woman and the tree, which was very ancient, recognises that woman was prakriti, the primal matter, the womb and the source of all creation.

The dream of the Salabhanjika stayed with Megha for a long time. Each time she saw a tree, she would think of the various rites that she had performed and she felt a close connection and bond with all trees. She also felt happy at being a young girl, who would grow up to contribute to the growth and prosperity of the world.

When Megha got up in the morning, the seed in the red cloth that Nani had given her was still in her hand, with her fingers tightly closed over it.

MEGHA AND THE SUFI SAINT
THE STORY OF THE SECOND MAGIC TREE

It was Megha's birthday. She was born on Ashtami, the eighth day of Navratri—the festival of nine nights. Megha's mother would always do something special on her birthday. Last year, she had taken her to the temple of Mahalaxmi and sitting in the courtyard of the temple, her mother had told her the story of the Samudra Manthan, the churning of the ocean. She told Megha how Laxmi, the Goddess of Wealth and Prosperity, had emerged from the ocean standing on a lotus. Before they came home, she had bought for Megha a print of Laxmi, which Megha hung on a wall in her bedroom. The year before that, her mother had taken her to a Jain temple and shown her the bhandara, where sacred books were kept, and then she related the story of the birth of Vardhaman Mahavira and the fourteen dreams of his mother, Trishala.

Megha dressed for her birthday

The parrot picks out a card for Megha

This year there was a Sufi festival in her town in honour of a Sufi saint and her mother took Megha to the Urs. Megha was thrilled to see all the fun and festivities. There was the bangle seller with multicoloured bangles and Megha tried out many bangles and picked out some red bangles for her little hands. And then there was the parrot astrologer who kept a parrot in a cage and when the parrot came out, it would pick out a card and the astrologer would read from that. Megha sat in front of the man and paid him a rupee. The astrologer opened the cage door and the parrot picked out a card which read, "It is your lucky day today. You will meet a godly person who will give you a gift." Megha chuckled with delight when she heard that. Next to the astrologer was a candy man and Megha bought pink candy floss. She enjoyed licking it and in no time it dissolved in her mouth and made her tongue pink. And then there was the monkey man who would rattle the little drum and the monkey would dance to its beat. Not far from there was a potter who was selling all sorts of clay objects: cups, earthen oil lamps called diyas, pots and toys, horses and elephants. Megha bought a small Bankura horse from him. The Bankura horse had a very long neck and it looked very cute to her. Around the corner was a small merry-go-round and Megha was fascinated to see plastic horses and elephants go round as the man turned the wheel and little children sitting on them giggled excitedly.

Finally, she saw a godman sitting cross legged under a large tree. Next to him was a grave on which was spread a green chaddar—a sheet of cloth. In front of him, he had spread out a mat with small bottles filled with pills, roots and many coloured seeds from different trees and plants. Megha was intrigued by this and asked her mother if she could go there. Her mother was a little hesitant at first but then agreed and the two of them went to the godman and began to talk to him. "I am a Sufi and a devotee of a Sufi saint who lived many years ago and who is buried here. I look after the grave and worship it twice a day. It brings me peace of mind and I feel blessed by the saint."

Megha asked him all about Sufi saints and the man spoke to her about Hazrat Khwaja Nizamuddin Auliya and his disciple, Amir Khusro, and how they had started a tradition of Sufi saints in India. "Have you ever been to Ajmer to the shrine of Hazrat Khwaja Gharib Nawaz?" he asked Megha. Megha was sitting on the ground and shook her head. "Someday you must go there and offer a chaddar of roses," said the man.

Just as they were about to leave, the godman gave Megha a small seed. It was dark brown and had a lot of ridges on it like the rudraksha bead of the japa mala. "Keep it with you and it will bring you a lot of peace." Megha accepted the seed and opened her little purse to pay him. The godman just smiled and said, "This is my gift to you. There is no price for gifts." Megha folded her hands and touched his feet and then holding her mother's hand started walking back home.

A magical tree grows from the Sufi saint's seed

Megha looks out from her window

All along, she kept on thinking of the seed and the Sufi saint. When they went home Megha's mother said, "Let's leave the seed in the garden. Don't take it inside. Who knows, it may have germs on it."

After dinner and a delicious gulab-jamun, an Indian dessert, Megha quietly disappeared in the garden and took the seed and hid it in the earth. She was afraid that a squirrel would eat it or take it away and she did not want to lose that precious seed. She finished her homework and fell asleep.

In the middle of the night, she heard a voice and woke up. It seemed to be coming from the garden. She got up and went outside and saw that a huge magical tree had grown where she had hidden the seed. Voices and music floated to her from the tree. Megha looked at the tree in amazement. She had never seen one like it before. Rising from the ground, it almost reached the sky and as it swayed in the wind, music and voices became louder and clearer.

At the root of the tree were multicoloured kalashas or vessels, some of clay, others of brass and copper and some even of silver and gold, and they were overflowing with fragrant water. All the kalashas were bright and shining and had red ribbons tied around them. And from each of them grew lotuses; some red, some white and others blue. Some lotuses were like a vine and they encircled the tree; others just grew out of the kalasha and went upwards and yet others spread on the ground. In some kalashas were mango leaves and in one kalasha were gold coins that overflowed and lay scattered all around it. She went closer to the kalashas and asked, "Who are you and what is your name?" A voice from one of the kalashas said, "We are the Amrit Kalashas, the pots of nectar from the ocean. We came to this world when the gods and the demons churned the ocean with the help of Vishnu. Some call us Purna Kumbha, which means we are always full. From us arise lotuses and the Kalpavriksha, the wish-fulfilling tree. In us is contained Amrit, the nectar of immortality. We are present in every home and in every puja." Megha was fascinated by the kalashas and she poured out a little water from them and drank it and felt blessed.

There was another voice. It came from the earth around the Magic Tree. The earth said, "I am Prithvi, the earth, the source of all that grows. In me are ancient footfalls of rishis, the great sages; within me are songs and stories of people; deep down within me there are springs of water which feed the lakes and rivers. I support the world; on me are paths and pavements where people move and also homes and hamlets where people live. I am the source of all that grows; on me are the fields and farms. In me are planted all the seeds and I hold them till they are ready to sprout to shrubs and trees. I am the Garbha, the womb of life; I am Prakriti, the primal matter. And underneath me is a giant tortoise which supports me."

Megha was spellbound by the voice of the earth. She walked gently on it and venerated it by touching it and then applied the dust from it to her forehead. She then drew a rangoli, a pattern with coloured powder, on it and the earth trembled and beautiful flowers grew from it as if to welcome Megha.

Megha looked at the tree again and she saw that there were many diyas and lanterns hanging from its branches. And then the tree spoke again.

"I am Agni, the fire that keeps everyone alive. I am the fire of the yajna, a ritual of sacrifice mentioned in the ancient scriptures called Vedas. I am the fire in the hearth of homes. I am the fire in the havan, where religious offerings are made; the light of the lamp that is lit in the temple. I am also the fire in the sun, creating the light of the day and the energy of the moon, which illuminates the night. I am the light of the stars that shine in the sky. I am the source of heat and radiance in the world. I am the fire in the body that makes it move and come alive. I make plants grow, leaves turn green, trees bear fruits. I give flowers their brilliant colours and fruits their sweet taste. I am the fire of flames that go upwards towards heaven but my heat and light illuminate the world. I am the fire of the little diyas that bring you the light of Diwali and also the light of the candles that are lit in the church. I am the fire in you that makes your eyes light up, and the energy in your mind that creates beautiful speech."

Megha took a diya that was hanging from the tree and did a small aarti—a prayer—for the Magic Tree, and the lights on the tree shone brightly on her as if to say that she was very special to it.

Megha sat on the earth and looked at the tree again. She saw many banners: the banner of Vishnu, the Preserver of the Universe with his vehicle Garuda on it and the banner of Kama, the God of Love with a parrot on it. There were many flags of different kings, each with their distinctive insignia, and also flags of the Buddhists with prayers written on them. There were odhnis of many colours—red and blue, orange and yellow. And there were multicoloured kites, and all of these were flying in the wind. The tree spoke again.

"I am the wind which carries prayers and messages; I carry Akashvani—the Word of Gods; I make the kites fly and I make the clouds move in the sky. I create ripples on lakes and rivers. I carry the prayers of the Buddhists from far and wide, from the stupas and monasteries, from hilltops and groves, from prayer wheels large and small, to the devout. I am the Meghdoot of Kalidasa who carried the message from the yaksha, the tree spirit, to his beloved. I am the soft breeze that carries the fragrance of sandalwood from the Malaya Mountains. I am the wind that delights the hearts of kite flyers on Makar Sankranti day. I am the wind that carries voices and songs, chants and prayers, for I am vak—sacred speech, and I reside in Saraswati, the Goddess of Learning and Music. I am also Hanuman, who flies in the wind as he serves Rama."

Megha stood in awe and reverence to the wind. Just then, there was a soft and fragrant breeze and she heard voices from far and near, from the past and the present, and she whispered a prayer to the wind.

There was yet another voice from the tree. This was from the top of the tree and when Megha looked up she saw the sun and the moon and stars on its branches. They shone brightly. There was a brilliant glow, as if a thousand suns were shining in the sky, and stars were shooting from one corner to another. There were multicoloured lights and twinkling lights and it looked as if there were fireworks in the sky. Here, there was no darkness and no night. Megha was amazed and wonderstruck. She heard a voice from the top of the tree.

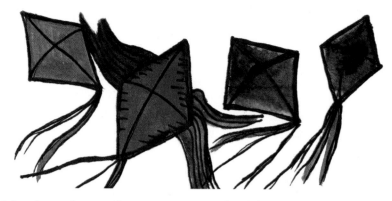

"I am Akasha, the infinite space. I hold within me the sun and the moon and the stars. I am vast and I am also the void. I am the limitless sky and what is above and beyond it. I am unending, without limits and borders. I am the abode of peace and tranquility. Here there are no sounds, no voices, no arguments, and no disputes. I am the Purna, the totality, the full, just enlightenment but no light or darkness; just bliss but no pleasure or pain; just pavitra or pure and neither good nor bad; just perfection and neither right nor wrong. Here there is sheer beauty and spiritual serenity. Here there are no birds but just the Raj Hamsa, the King of Swans, who flies in space to go to Kailasa. The Raj Hamsa is very clever for it can separate milk from water. In my space reside the Gandharvas who play celestial music.

Megha was spellbound by the voice of Akasha. She raised her arms to reach it but could not, so she folded her hands in reverence and prayer.

Just then, the Sufi saint who had given her the seed, came there and touched her head with his hand to bless her and said, "This tree is the Kalpavriksha, the wish-fulfilling tree. See how it has grown. It rises from water, touches the earth, contains fire, holds wind and finally reaches space. This is a replica of how you should be, how you should think and live. You should be rooted

Kalashas, diyas and flowers adorn the tree

Celestial birds on the Magic Tree

in the earth, which means to abide in your family traditions and religion, follow and respect the customs and culture of your parents. Like the water, you should be serene and gentle and keep on flowing and evolving. Remember that the river starts in the mountain and ends in the ocean and like the river, your life is a long journey. Like the wind, be brave and courageous; just as the wind carries pollen from one flower to another be generous and helpful; like the wind carry messages of love and joy to everyone. And then there is Agni or fire; radiant, bright and the giver of light and heat; be like it—full of energy and radiance in everything you do. And finally, there is Akasha or space, vast and without boundaries and which holds within it the sun and the moon. Be like the sky, open your mind and heart to everyone, be fearless and without anger, be light of mind and spirit and above all, be happy and like the sky, spread happiness everywhere you go."

Megha heard the Sufi saint in rapt attention. She touched the tree and then gave it a big hug, and in turn, the tree showered petals of flowers on her till her head was covered with them. She felt blessed.

When Megha woke up in the morning, she went and got the seed from where she had hidden it. She kept it in the box where she had kept the first seed.

Megha watching out for the birds

MEGHA AND THE CELESTIAL BIRDS
THE STORY OF THE THIRD MAGIC TREE

Megha was very fond of birds. She would look at them with great joy and admiration. They were her playmates. She would often talk to them and tell them stories, although she was not sure that they would understand her. Outside her room in the garden there was a large Pipal tree and she had hung a small bird feeder on it. She would be thrilled to see little mynah birds come and perch on it and eat seeds. Early in the morning, as the sun was rising, they would chitter-chatter and this would wake her up in time for school. How lucky that was, for then she did not need an alarm clock.

Just under the tree she had kept a bird bath and she would always fill it with water. When birds came there to have their bath, she would watch them with great fondness. The way they sat on the bath, dipped their wings in the water and then fluttered them would bring a lot of joy to her.

Before going to school, she would make sure that the bird feeder was full of seeds and when she ran out of seeds, she would remind her mother to get some more from the market. Many of Megha's toys were shaped like animals and she was particularly fond of her wooden parrot.

One day, she saw the birds gathering little sticks and making a nest in the tree. She wondered how without any hands they were so skilled in making an artistic nest. They would bend the sticks with their beaks and weave them by going round and round till a small basket was made. When the nest was ready, the birds laid two eggs in it. She would see one bird sitting on the eggs, and then one day, two little birds chirped in the nest. The mother bird brought seeds and then fed the little birds with her beak. How Megha wished she could feed them too but she did not go near the nest in case the young birds got frightened. And a few weeks later the little ones began to fly and left the nest, never to come back. Megha was saddened and worried about the birds but her mother told her that the birds would be safe and that they were capable of looking after themselves. This satisfied Megha but she would still look to see if the birds came back to the tree.

Under the Pipal tree, pigeons would come and rest and eat the seeds that had fallen from the bird feeder. Megha would spread some seeds on the earth for the pigeons. She loved the cooing of the pigeons and the way they walked nodding their heads. Once she had some seeds in her hand and a pigeon came and sat there to eat the seeds. Megha wanted to take the pigeon to her room but he flew away.

Parrots would also come and sit on the tree. Megha loved their green plume and red beaks. Parrots would not talk much but they would love to sit in pairs and nibble on the fruits that grew on the tree. She had learnt from her mother that parrots liked peanuts and chana dal, a lentil, and she would keep these in a small cup at the bottom of the tree.

And then there were crows. They were very restless and would not sit too long, and they would make a lot of noise. It seemed that they were always looking for food, mostly for insects in the ground. Their large black beaks could dig deep and Megha wondered how they knew where the insects were. Once, when she threw a piece of bread, many crows came to claim it and they began fighting with each other.

Occasionally, a very large bird would come and sit on the highest branch of the tree. It was an eagle and he wanted always to be at the top for he felt that he was the king of birds and would not accept a lower place. From his spot high on the tree, the eagle could see the whole world and when he flew, he would go high in the sky till one could see him no more.

And then there were two white birds who would sit together. They were very different for it seemed that they were in search of something special. Their feathers were always wet and they would look at the sky. Megha did not know their names and was very curious.

One cold day, a large white bird flew into Megha's garden and she was quite surprised. She had never seen this bird before and her mother told her that he had come from Kailasa where Shiva lived. It was a hamsa—a swan.

Not far from the tree there was a peacock. He would walk about gracefully, showing off his bright blue feathers.

Megha wanted to know more about all these different birds and she asked the school librarian who gave her a book on various birds. She read all the books that she could find in her school

library about birds, but she wanted to know more. She wanted to talk to the birds, learn their language and understand the songs they sang. She wanted to know how they could fly away from their nest and come back at the end of the day. What would they do when they were hungry or tired? Where did they sleep? There were no answers to her many questions.

One day, Megha's sleep was disturbed as she heard sounds from her garden. She went to her window and saw that there were many different birds on the tree. The birds were talking to each other and when they saw Megha at the window they said, "Come out and talk to us. We have come specially for you."

Megha went to the garden making sure not to wake her mother and sat under the tree. One by one, the birds came down and sat next to her and spoke to her and told her their stories.

First came the pigeon. He had grey and white feathers. He sat next to Megha and said:

"I am a pigeon from Lucknow and along with my brothers and sisters, I play games with people. People in Lucknow go to their terraces and release us in the air and then they make different bird sounds and call us and we go back to them. On festive days, there are competitions to see whose pigeon goes farthest and then comes back. You see, we have little magnetic devices in our head which tell us exactly where our home is, no matter how far we go. That is why we are always able to come back. Did you know that Wajid Ali Shah, the nawab of Awadh had a thousand pigeons and every time he walked outside in the garden, we would form a canopy over him. Sometimes we were used as messengers."

Megha enjoyed listening to the pigeon. She gave him some seeds and the pigeon flew away. Then came the parrot and sat next to Megha and spoke:

"I am the parrot from the *Shuka Saptati*, the seventy stories of a parrot. I belonged to a merchant by the name of Khojasta. One day, when he was leaving for business, he told me to look after his wife. Every evening, I would tell her a story and she would listen with great interest and I would keep on telling her stories till she fell asleep. That way I would make sure that the wife did not leave home to meet someone else. I did this for a whole month and when the merchant returned, he was pleased to see that I had done what he had asked me to do and he rewarded me. I am also the vehicle of Kama, the God of Love, and carry him on my back."

Megha was fascinated by the stories of the parrot. She gave him some peanuts and he flew away.

Then came the crow and he flew down from the branch and sat next to Megha and spoke:

The parrot from *Shuka Saptati*

The parrot is a celestial vehicle of the gods

"I am the common crow and I announce the arrival of guests. I know where to find lonely women who are separated from their beloved. I fly in the sky looking for the beloved and when I find him, I go to the home of the lonely woman and tell her that he will be here soon. Once, I sat on the window of a queen who was waiting for her beloved. She promised me that she would paint my beak in gold and make kheer, a sweet pudding, for me and give it to me in a silver bowl. In a previous birth I was a brahmin but was cursed to be a crow. But once I saw the child Rama, I chose to remain a crow and live near Manasarovar to spread Rama bhakti—adoration of Rama. I told his story once even to Garuda. That story is still called *Bhusandi Ramayana* after my name."

Megha enjoyed listening to the crow and gave him a laddu and the crow flew away.

Then came the peacock. He flew down from the branch and stood next to Megha and performed a dance and then spoke:

"I am the peacock from Vrindavana, the forest where Krishna lives. I walk and dance around Krishna and the gopis. When clouds gather in the sky and it is about to rain, I spread my feathers and perform the rain dance. The gopis also dance with me in joy. Look at my feathers. How nice and blue they are, and right in the middle, there is a sun. Krishna wears one of my feathers in his crown and I feel blessed because of that. When Krishna and the gopis perform the Rasa, I sit on the tree and watch them go round and round. When the gopis are lonely without Krishna, I keep them company and assure them that Krishna will be with them soon. Do you know Kartikeya, the son of Shiva—Destroyer and Renewer of the Universe? Kartikeya is also called Murugan. He sits on me and I carry him all around."

Megha enjoyed talking to the peacock and gave him some seeds. The peacock flew away but left behind a feather for her.

Then came the eagle. He swooped down and sat close to Megha and spoke:

The peacock from Krishna's Vrindavan is the vehicle of Kartikeya

The mighty Garuda; vehicle of Vishnu

"I am Garuda, the King of Birds. I fly high in the sky. I am the vehicle of Vishnu and I am at his service all the time. Vishnu looks after this world and all his devotees and whenever they are in difficulty, Vishnu comes to their rescue, and I carry him everywhere speedily. When Gajendra, the elephant, was captured by the crocodile, it is I who took Vishnu there. And when Krishna wanted to take the Parijataka tree from Indra's heaven and bring it down, it is I who carried him safely back to earth. And when Aniruddha was captured by Banasura, it is I who took Krishna, with his brother Balarama and his son Pradyumna to Shonitpur to rescue Aniruddha."

Megha was touched by these stories of Garuda and said "Jai ho! Hail Vishnu!"

Next came the two white birds that were sitting on the top. They came down and sat next to Megha and said:

"We are the last two of the eight Brahmaputras. We live near the holy river Ganga in Varanasi and after our bath in the river in the morning, we come to Pakshiteertham in Thirukalukundram near Kanchipuram at noon where devotees give us food. We then go to Rameshwaram for a darshan—blessings from the deity—and rest at the temple of Chidambaram for the night. We are devotees of Shiva and find happiness in serving Him."

Megha was touched by the story of the two white birds. She folded her hands and said, "Om Namoh Shivaya—Hail Shiva."

Then came the majestic hamsa and he too came down and sat besides Megha and spoke:

"I am the Raj Hamsa, the King of Swans. I fly high in the sky and go to Kailasa in the Himalayas which is where Shiva lives. In my beak I carry a lotus stalk. I connect both the water on the earth and the sky above. I can separate milk from water. People create my image on top of temple lamps and they give my name to sages and saints and call them Paramahamsa, the Supreme Swan or the one who has attained enlightenment. Saraswati sits on me. I carry her everywhere, whenever she wants to visit other gods."

Megha was touched by the words of the hamsa and she folded her hands in prayer and the hamsa flew away.

The tree was now empty and Megha returned to her room and fell asleep. When she got up in the morning, she thought of all the birds that she had seen in her dream the night before and recollected all their stories. The next time she saw these birds anywhere, they would seem so much closer to her. They had now become her lifelong friends.

Saraswati sits on the beautiful Raj Hamsa

MEGHA AND THE MAGICAL PARROT
THE STORY OF THE FOURTH MAGIC TREE

Megha loved her school and of all the subjects, she loved History and Geography the most. In one of her Geography classes, the teacher was describing various pilgrimages in our country. Pilgrimages, she said, were important for many reasons. They took people to different parts of India to visit and worship at various shrines and temples. Not only did people come to understand all religious stories and traditions but felt blessed by the presiding deity of each temple. People who undertook pilgrimages also learnt about the history of the temples, heard accounts of the saints and holy men who visited those temples, and came to know about the patrons who built them.

Around the temples there are shops and stores, there are crafts people and artists who make various objects which the pilgrims take home as remembrances of their visit and to give as gifts to their friends and relatives. And people who receive these gifts treasure them in their home shrines and feel blessed. There are also a lot of food and flower shops around the temples where devotees buy sweets as an offering. During pilgrimages, people from all over India meet each other and they come to understand various different customs and hear different languages.

Megha raised her hand as the teacher was speaking.

"How long would it take to do all the pilgrimages?" she asked eagerly.

"It would take many lives to go to all the important temples in India. We are a god-loving people and we have made so many temples during the last two thousand years. Many of them have become pilgrimage sites," the teacher said.

The teacher continued her talk and Megha remained spellbound by the accounts of all the pilgrimages.

"You must not treat pilgrimages as picnics or holidays as there is a very important reason why you should go on a pilgrimage. Pilgrimages are called tirtha yatras or a journey where you cross a river or a ford. The whole purpose of going on a pilgrimage is to transform and change your mind, to make your mind pure and godly, in other words, to make you a better person."

Mount Kailasa is the abode of Shiva

Megha was very moved by the teacher's talk on pilgrimages. Over dinner she spoke to her mother about this and asked when they would undertake a pilgrimage. Her mother told her that once Megha finished school, she would take her on a pilgrimage.

Megha finished her homework, but at the back of her mind were stories of pilgrimages. She thought a lot about what the teacher had taught her that day. She wanted to meet all the gods and goddesses of our country and she wished she would grow up soon so that she could go and visit them. Thinking of this, Megha fell asleep.

In the middle of the night there was a sound outside her window and she saw a parrot on the branch of the Pipal tree in the garden, ringing a bell that she had hung only the week before. It was a bell that her aunt had brought for her when she returned from a pilgrimage. The parrot had beautiful green feathers, a large red beak and round eyes. It said, "I am Shukraj, the magic parrot. I have been sent here by my master to take you on a pilgrimage. Come with me. I will become a plane and take you wherever you want to go."

Megha was both surprised and excited. Who was this Shukraj and where did he come from? How will I be able to sit on him? Will he bring me back home? Should I tell my mother about this? She thought about all this and decided to look outside the window and she was even more surprised when she saw that the parrot had become a plane. The parrot would fly up with her, into the sky.

Shukraj saw Megha at the window and said, "Come, I am ready for you."

Megha quickly got dressed and remembered to take her odhni in case it got very windy in the sky. She was excited but a little frightened too.

Shukraj said, "Fasten your seat belt and if you are scared as we fly, hold on to me." So saying, he took off. Very soon they were up in the air and from high up in the sky she could see her home and thought of her mother.

"Where are we going?" Megha asked

"We are going to Kailasa, the abode of Shiva in the Himalayas. Shiva is our foremost god and he lives in Kailasa with his consort Parvati. His trusted servant Nandi, the bull, is always by his side. And from the peaks of Kailasa, Shiva watches over all of India and takes care of all of us. It is here that Shiva performed the Ananda Tandava, the Dance of Bliss. Look at the mountains and the snow-covered peaks. And do you see the bird that is flying above the peak? That is the Raj Hamsa who flies several thousand miles northward to reach Kailasa to finally rest here."

Megha looked ahead and as she saw the sun rise on the snow-covered peaks of the Himalayas, she was thrilled. The early morning sun made the mountains golden. Megha had never seen these mountains from so close and she was captivated by the beauty of it all.

"Where is Shiva?" she asked.

The Manasarovar Lake

"Shiva is invisible to us. He has to be experienced and felt within oneself. We must have a strong sense of faith. And once you have completed all the pilgrimages and performed your duties, you will surely see Him," Shukraj said.

"And what about Parvati?" she asked.

"Parvati is always with Shiva, tending to his every need. She is his Shakti, his strength.

"Can you see the beautiful lake? It is Manasarovar, the most sacred lake for Hindus and Buddhists. It is believed that all our rivers arise from it. Do you see the pilgrims going around the lake? Notice how still is the water of the lake; it is clear blue, reflecting the sky in it. That is how our mind should be. For only in a clear mind can you experience Shiva.

"Look at the pilgrims walking with sticks and with a backpack. They have come from all parts of India for this pilgrimage and have been walking for a month. Kailasa is special not only to the Hindus but also to the Buddhists and Jains. These pilgrims have walked on little winding paths, over stone and dirt and slept in tents along the way. It is hard work to keep on walking but it is their faith that keeps them going. And can you see the pilgrims carrying flags? They are Buddhists and have come from Nepal and Tibet."

"Do they not get tired, walking so much?" Megha asked with some concern.

"Yes, they do! It is part of the experience of a pilgrimage. One must put the body through hardship for only then does the mind become pure.

Pilgrims overcome many hardships to reach the abode of the Lord

"Look at those pilgrims. They are performing a puja on the shores of the lake. And when they complete the puja, they will take some water from the lake back with them in a small bottle."

Megha was beside herself with excitement to have been a part of this pilgrimage, even if aerially.

She held on to Shukraj and looked longingly at the Kailasa Mountain and saw three ridges on it, which looked like Shiva's trident. Alongside it, snow had formed the letter 'Om'.

"I think it is time to take you back home. Some other time, I will take you to another pilgrimage of Shiva at Amarnath in Kashmir," Shukraj said, and as he did so, the plane sped off and Megha sat holding on to him.

"Is there a lake there too?" Megha asked.

"No, but there you will see Shiva as a lingam, one of his forms, made of snow."

When the plane landed in Megha's garden, Shukraj gave her a big hug and said that he would return the next day. Megha quietly slipped into her bed and fell asleep.

All day she thought about Kailasa and Manasarovar and made a pledge that when she grew up, she would surely go there.

A few days passed and she heard the same bell in the middle of the night. When she went to the window, she saw Shukraj again. He waved to her and Megha quickly got ready. When she went to her garden, Shukraj gave her a big hug and helped her to sit on the plane.

"Today I will take you to another mountain pilgrimage. This is also in the Himalayas and is dedicated to Vishnu," he said.

"I thought we were going to Amarnath to see the snow lingam," said Megha.

"Unfortunately one can only go there on the full moon of Shravan, the season of prayer, when the snow lingam is formed."

"Why are there so many pilgrimage sites in mountains?" asked Megha curiously.

"Because our gods like to live in mountains and the Himalayas are our most sacred mountains. They also live in caves and in forests. You see, we have to find our gods, travel to their abodes, make an effort to go and visit them. That is the idea of a pilgrimage. In a pilgrimage, the journey is as important as the destination. That is why it is called a tirtha yatra, the crossing of a ford. A pilgrimage is similar to the journey of life. In a pilgrimage you have to cross a ford to meet the gods, just as in life, you have to cross a lot of obstacles to succeed."

"Will my journey on a plane with you count as a pilgrimage?" Megha asked.

"Of course it will. Once I have shown you these pilgrimage sites, you will go to them when you grow up and you will know it all," Shukraj said, reassuring Megha.

They flew over the Ganga and she saw Haridwar and Rishikesh and many pilgrims taking a dip in the river and filling their jars with the sacred water of the holy river to take home. And as the plane flew higher, they were in the foothills of the

Buddhist Monastery

Himalayas, dotted with small towns along rivers. These were mountain rivers and tributaries and it seemed as if their waters were gushing down in a hurry to join the Ganga. Those little towns along the gushing rivers were quaint. There was a certain peace about them. She saw people covered with shawls walking the narrow streets and there were many temples along the rivers. She wondered whether living so close to a mountain changes the way you think. She also saw a number of pilgrims walking along winding pathways, many with sticks and some barefoot, some on horseback and others who were carried in a chair by four men.

Just then, the plane landed in a very large courtyard surrounded by snow-covered mountains and there was a large and imposing temple in front of her. Megha was in the midst of many people wanting to go inside the temple. In spite of the noise and clamour, she felt a certain peace for she was at the abode of the gods.

"This is the temple of Badrinath, where Vishnu lives," Shukraj said, escorting Megha through the crowds, and after waiting in line and jostling with the crowds, they were able to get a darshan of the idol. It was covered with many flowers. In the couple of minutes she was there, Megha could catch only a glimpse of the idol. Shukraj explained that it was the idol or a murti of Vishnu that Adi Shankara had found in the river and that it was he who'd had this temple built.

Megha mingled with the crowds and saw the many shops that lined the narrow road leading up to the temple. There were flower shops and sweetmeat shops, shops selling souvenirs and others selling beads. She had remembered the bead that Nani had given her and she bought a bead for herself and kept it in her pocket.

"Why is it that I could not see the face of the murti?" Megha asked as she was getting on the plane.

"It is because the idol is a bit damaged and Adi Shankara, who discovered the idol in the river, stipulated that it be covered with sandalwood paste every morning by the temple priests. This is the morning ritual at Badrinath."

"What happens to all the sandalwood paste that is removed from the idol?"

"That becomes the prasad that the devotee takes home and I have brought some for you," Shukraj gave her a small packet. Megha clutched it to her chest and they flew back home.

The visit to Badrinath was on Megha's mind all day and she decided to go there when she was older and she would walk all the way up and not go by a plane.

Several days passed and there was no sign of Shukraj. Megha was beginning to miss him and the beautiful experience of the pilgrimages. She had borrowed some books from the library and while reading about Shiva and Vishnu, she fell asleep. Then she heard the bell and ran to the window and was delighted to see Shukraj. She went out into the garden and asked Shukraj, "Where have you been? I have waited every night for you."

The temple of Badrinath, one of Vishnu's abodes

"I was busy taking an old mother to a pilgrimage to Vaishno Devi and that is where we are going today."

Megha was delighted and quickly got ready and sat on Shukraj and in no time they were in the sky. This time they flew over the Kashmir valley and once they had passed Jammu, they saw small towns. Soon she saw a lot of pilgrims walking up the winding paths. Many were walking barefoot, some had canes, others were being carried on palanquins and some were on horseback. There were many small shrines along the way, where pilgrims would stop and pray, then keep walking. All along the way there were shops and places to eat, where pilgrims would stop and rest and refresh themselves.

"Can I get down and walk with the pilgrims?" she asked Shukraj excitedly.

"No, we do not have that much time. When you come here when you are older, you will be able to walk like other pilgrims."

Megha was disappointed but soon they landed in front of the temple. She was struck by the atmosphere of the place. It had a certain aroma, there was the sound of temple bells, the sight of people greeting each other and, all in all, there was a certain sacredness here. "Why can't every place be like this?" she wondered. Very soon she was in the sanctum of the Vaishno Devi temple. It was dark and mysterious and in the light of an oil lamp, she could see three stones covered with flowers and the face of the goddess. This was the sacred Vaishno Devi. She folded her hands in awe and reverence and said a prayer and applied a kumkum tilak on her forehead from a small bowl that was kept there. Shukraj was keeping an eye on her to make sure that she did not get lost in the surging crowd. They went out in the streets and Megha bought green bangles for herself and put them on right away. This was to be her prasad.

Shukraj asked her to get on his back and soon they were flying back home.

Megha hid the bangles under her pillow along with the bead that she had brought from Badrinath and the small bottle of water from Manasarovar.

Several days passed and Megha thought of all the pilgrimages that she had been to: Kailasa, Badrinath and Vaishno Devi. She kept on thinking of the various pilgrimages that Shukraj had taken her to and realised there are two journeys in every pilgrimage, an actual journey and a spiritual journey. Along with the body, the mind travels too, and both the mind and the body need to be blessed and purified and transformed during a pilgrimage. She was touched by the shrines of Shiva, Vishnu and Devi. How rich is our Indian tradition, she felt. But these were all Hindu temples. What about the other religions? Where do their devotees go on a pilgrimage? She thought of this all day.

That night when the bell rang she was all ready and even before Shukraj could invite her, she was sitting on the plane with him.

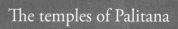

The temples of Palitana

"Take me to a Jain pilgrimage today," she said. "You are reading my mind," said Shukraj, "I am taking you to a Jain pilgrimage." Megha chirped, "I would like that as my friend Bhanu is a Jain and I want to understand her religion."

Shukraj took to the sky and very soon they were flying over the Shatrunjaya Mountain in Gujarat. She could see a number of white temples on this mountain and their spires were bathed in the golden light of the rising sun. Shukraj explained to Megha a little bit of the Jain tradition, how ancient it was, of their 24 tirthankaras and of Mahavira who was the last tirthankara. "The Jains believe in ahimsa or non-violence and this is their credo."

"Who are those people dressed in white, who have covered their faces with a mask and carry a broom with them?" asked Megha as she saw pilgrims making their way up.

"Those are Jain sadhus and they wear a mask as they do not want to kill any insect that may accidentally enter their mouth. They carry a broom as they do not want to step on an insect either as they walk. For the same reason they do not eat anything that grows under the soil like potatoes," Shukraj was busy explaining the tenets of Jainism. And Megha was listening attentively. She was glad that she was a vegetarian but decided that she was going to apply the Jain doctrine of ahimsa to everything in life.

Shukraj circled around all temples on the Shatrunjaya Mountain and even from this height, Megha was touched by the splendour of the temples of Palitana and the dedication and austerity of the barefoot Jain sadhus who were making their way up. The top of the mountain was dotted with a hundred temples in white stone. She had never seen so many temples in one place. She decided that she would get a book from her library and read all about the Jains and on Mahavira in particular. It was quite windy and Shukraj did not land on the mountain but flew low so that Megha could get a good look at all the temples. After she was satisfied with the aerial darshan of this Jain pilgrimage site, they returned home.

Megha was not able to get a souvenir from Palitana so she asked her mother to get her an image of Mahavira. Her mother was a little surprised as Megha had never talked about Mahavira before. Megha just smiled and said that her friend was a Jain and she wanted to know all about her gods. She pasted this picture on the wall in front of her desk.

The next day when she met Bhanu, she had a lot of questions for her and during the lunch recess, she spoke to the librarian and asked her for a book on Jainism. She was now quite excited about various pilgrimages and marked Kailasa, Badrinath, Vaishno Devi and Shatrunjaya with a red marker on a map of India. She looked at the map and realised that all these four pilgrimage sites were in the north and the west of India. "Are there not any pilgrimage sites in the south of India?" she wondered. She decided that she would ask Shukraj this question. She slept with this thought on her mind and, lo and behold, Shukraj appeared in the middle of the night and rang the bell. Megha got ready and sat on Shukraj and asked immediately, "Are there no pilgrimage sites in the

Jain ritual cloth

A page from *Kalpasutra*, a Jain sacred text

south of India?" Shukraj smiled and said, "I can read your mind! Today I am taking you to Shabarimala. It is in the southern state of Kerala." And even as he was talking, Shukraj had taken to the air and was flying southward. Very soon he was flying over the Western Ghats and Megha could see the mountains and the Arabian Sea and the lush landscape of Kerala.

Shabarimala is the home of Ayappa, the son of Harihara, a form of Shiva and Vishnu. Ayappa demands very strict observances from his devotees. They must live with a guru for a month before starting this pilgrimage to clean their body and purify their mind, eat simple food and wear white or black clothes.

"That is very difficult!" Megha exclaimed, looking down on the Shabarimala Mountain. She saw many pilgrims dressed in black climbing the mountain, some alone and the others in groups. There was a certain peace and quiet; the pilgrims had a happy look on their faces as they climbed the mountain. Megha wished she could be on the ground and walk with them. Just then Shukraj flew very low over the shrine and she saw a line of devotees entering the temple. Shukraj landed in a corner and Megha got down and saw the throngs of people from a distance. She did not see any girl so she decided not to join the line but stood there with folded hands and closed eyes, and prayed. How she wished she could go into the shrine and get a darshan of Ayappa. Shukraj waved to her and this was his signal that she should return as it was time to go back. He gave her some flowers and said that these were from the shrine. She tucked them inside her choli as she did not want to lose them. Soon Shukraj flew in the air and Megha could see the mountain and the sea and once again she whispered a prayer. Shukraj landed in Megha's garden and she bid a sad farewell to him.

Devotees light large lamps at the temple of Ayappa

The temple of Ayappa

"When will you come back?" she asked.

"Very soon," he said, patting her on the back.

Megha went to her room and, clutching the flowers from Shabarimala, fell asleep.

By now Megha was getting familiar with all the pilgrimages and their rituals and realised their importance in the life of a devotee. The peace and calm on the faces of the pilgrims told her that this was the result of being a pilgrim. She had so many questions and even more, she wished to visit all the pilgrimage sites in India. But then, there was homework to do as examinations were drawing close and there was also her mother and the rest of the family with whom she wanted to spend time, so she pushed these thoughts to the back of her mind.

She kept hoping that she would meet Shukraj one more time and her wish came true. When she heard the bell, Megha ran towards him and had so much to tell him. But before she could do that, Shukraj spoke:

"I know you want to go to all the pilgrimage sites in India along with me. There are so many holy places in India that an entire life would not be sufficient. There is Pandharpur in Maharashtra, home of Vitthal; there is Kamakshi in Assam where a goddess resides; there is the Golden Temple in Amritsar, the holiest shrine of the Sikhs; there is Bodh Gaya in Bihar where Buddha attained nirvana—freedom from the circle of life and death; there is Mount Mary in Mumbai where Christians worship and then there is Ajmer which is the shrine of the Sufi saint Khwaja Gharib Nawaz. There are countless shrines and temples, churches and mosques, monasteries and ashrams where people go to find

God." Megha was listening attentively.

"When will I be able to go to all these pilgrimages?"

"First you must grow up and finish studying, then you must marry and have a family and look after it. When you get a call from these gods in pilgrimages, it shall be your time to go there. You cannot go on a pilgrimage without being called."

"How will I know that the gods are calling me to come to them?"

"When you have an intense desire to go on a pilgrimage and all your plans fall into place quickly, then that is your signal that God is calling you.

"I have another call today, which I must listen to. Khojasta is going away for a month and he wants me to look after his wife while he is away. I have promised to be with her and tell her a story every night till she falls asleep. But I will never forget you for you are very special to me. Take this feather from my wing and keep it with you and anytime you want to talk to me, just place this feather between your two hands and I will come to you." Shukraj gave Megha a big hug, then blessed her by touching his wing to her head and flew away.

Megha stood there till she could see Shukraj no more and then holding the feather that he had given her, she went to her room and slept.

Megha and Shukraj

MEGHA AND NARADA
THE STORY OF THE FIFTH MAGIC TREE

It was a Sunday morning and since Megha had finished her homework, her mother and she decided to take a walk. It was drizzling and even though Megha had her umbrella, she did not open it. She enjoyed the rain so she walked without opening her umbrella, while her mother opened hers. The trees looked so fresh in the rainy season. It seemed that someone had washed all the leaves. The cuckoos sang melodiously and as Megha and her mother were walking, they came upon a medicine man sitting under a Pipal tree. He had spread out his jadi-butis—ayurvedic herbs—on a gunny bag. Megha stopped and began looking at the assortment of seeds and roots, branches and shoots, leaves and berries. She asked her mother what these were.

Megha climbs the Magic Tree

"Let us talk to the medicine man," said her mother.

"Sir, do tell us more about these seeds and roots. Where are they from and what is their purpose?"

The medicine man said to them, "I live in the Himalayas and these seeds and roots are from rare and special plants." He pointed to a small red berry and said, "This seed is good for digestion. And this root, when eaten with honey, removes joint pains."

He kept on showing all his Himalayan medicines and their uses but Megha kept looking at a large oval brown seed, as large as a biscuit. She picked it up and asked, "What is this?"

"This is a magic seed from a tree that grows next to a Buddhist monastery in the Himalayas. The monks use these in their prayers. I managed to get just one and it has been blessed by the monks," said the man.

"Can I take this seed, please?" Megha looked pleadingly at her mother.

Her mother hesitated and then half-heartedly agreed. She opened her purse and wanted to pay for it when the medicine man said, "This is my gift to your daughter. No one has ever

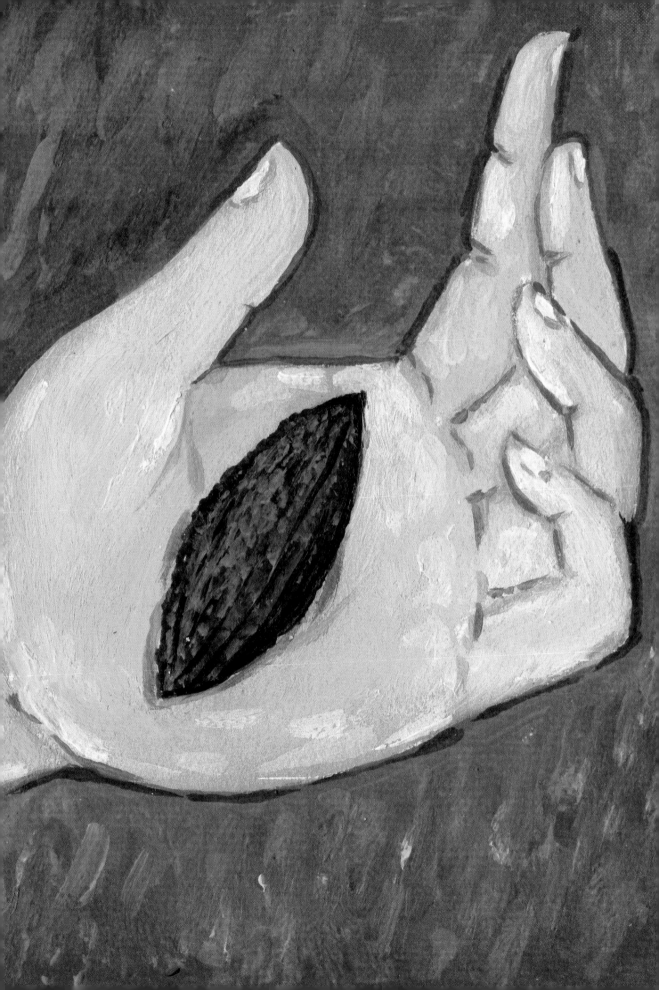

asked for it. It will bring her good fortune." So saying he gave the large brown seed to Megha who gratefully accepted it with both her hands.

As they reached home, Megha's mother asked her to look at the large brown seed that she had brought.

"I am not sure that we should take this seed inside the house. It has come from a monastery and may carry a curse with it," she said to Megha.

Megha began to cry, "A monastery is a home of gods, why should a curse come from there? Instead it will bring a blessing."

Her mother was adamant about the seed not entering the house. "The only thing I will let you do is to plant it in our garden."

Megha went to the garden and planted the seed under the bedroom window. Her mother was getting impatient with her fascination with seeds, that too from strangers. Megha felt sad that she could not bring the seed into the house. She ate dinner very quickly, did not speak a word and went to her room.

She woke up to the sound of rustling leaves, a musical sound that she had never heard before. It sounded as if a hundred flutes were playing together. She went to the window and, to her surprise, saw that a large tree with golden leaves had sprung up in the garden. The trunk of the tree was red and on it there were small branches which looked like steps. The tree was so high that she could not see where it ended. Megha stood amazed at this magic tree. Why were its leaves golden and its trunk red and what was the purpose of those step-like branches on the trunk? Was this

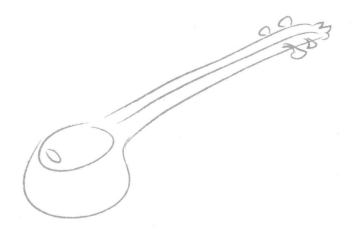

some sort of ladder to heaven? Was this an invitation from the Buddhist monks to go to heaven? She was wonderstruck and went outside and stood under the tree and the tree beckoned to her. She felt a strange closeness to the tree, as if it were a friend calling her. She went closer and hugged the tree and she heard a sweet voice from high up in the tree.

"Come, climb the tree and I will take you to heaven."

Megha put her foot on the first branch and very soon she climbed several branches and soon the sky with beautiful colours came into view. There were red and yellow streaks in the sky and maroon-coloured clouds floating gently. The wind was soft and fragrant, the air pleasant and the light luminous. She felt that she had left the earth and was in a higher world. Just then, a godly figure appeared before her. He was holding a tanpura, a stringed instrument, and said, "Narayan! Narayan! I am Narada, and I am the Messenger of the Gods. Welcome to our world."

Megha was delighted to see this divine figure. "What is this world which is so full of light?"

"This is Deva Loka, the world of celestial beings. This is a world in between the world of humans from where you come, and heaven which is the world of gods and goddesses. Our duty is to serve the gods and goddesses but I shuttle between heaven and earth and even go to the netherworld. I am a devotee of Vishnu and I go wherever He commands me to go. I promote bhakti or devotion to Vishnu and sing His praise."

Megha folded her hands and said that she would like to meet the celestial beings of Deva Loka.

"Come with me. Let us climb this tree together." When they climbed a few steps they came upon a beautiful person with a musical instrument. "This is a Gandharva," said Narada, "and they are the Musicians of the Gods. They live in the scents and the sap of barks and blossoms and can fly in the air playing music. People on earth seek their blessings before the start of a music performance." Megha did a namaskar and the Gandharva sang a beautiful song just for her. Megha was pleased and took his leave.

A Vidyadhar is a celestial being with magical powers

Kubera, the Treasurer of the Gods

Kinnara, a horse-headed celestial being

Garuda, the King of Birds

"Let us go one step higher," Narada said. Megha followed him and they came upon a beautiful person wearing a garland. "This is a Vidyadhar," Narada said. "Vidyadhars acquired magical powers when they drank the milk of the wish-fulfilling cow, Surabhi. They are always happy and bring joy to the gods and goddesses." Megha smiled at the Vidyadhar and he flew away in the sky to his home in the Himalayas.

Megha climbed a few more steps on the tree and came upon a dwarf-like person with a pot belly and a sack over his shoulder. "I am Kubera, Treasurer of the Gods. Vishwakarma, the Divine Architect, built a home of gold for me in Lanka but when Ravana captured Lanka, Vishwakarma built another home for me in Alkapuri in the Himalayas. I ride in the Pushpaka chariot and my duty is to ensure that the coffers of the gods are always full." Megha did a humble namaskar and Kubera gave her a gold coin.

Narada told Megha, "We have to climb higher still." They came upon a large bird with a human body and the bird said, "I am Garuda, the vehicle of Vishnu. Come with me and I will take you to Vaikuntha the celestial abode of Vishnu. Vaikuntha is a city of sparkling jewels and golden streets, dancing girls, of trees which sing and flowers that chant mantras." Megha looked at Narada and asked if they could go there. Narada said that he would take her there another time.

Just then two horse-headed people came flying by and said hello to Megha. "We are Kinnaras and we love each

other and are always together. Nothing can separate us. We love music and are happy to be with our gods and goddesses and play music in their homes." Megha was happy to meet them and asked if they would play a tune for her which they did, and in turn, Megha sang a song she had learnt in school. The pair of Kinnaras flew away and Megha could hear their sweet music much after they were gone.

Megha's eyes were beaming with what she saw in the sky on top of the tree. She wondered why she had never seen them before in her home or school. She turned to Narada and asked him, "What should I do to make these celestial beings come down to earth?" Narada said that they were very busy tending to the needs of the gods and goddesses in heaven but one could try and send them a message. "How do we do that?" Narada summoned an Apsara, a celestial beauty, and she came flying towards them. Her name was Rambha and she had risen from the ocean when the gods had churned it. She had an angelic face, two wings and was carrying a golden pot in her hand. She came close to Megha and gave her a big hug and Megha smiled and touched her feet. "What is in the golden pot?" she asked.

"This is the Amrit Kalasha, the pot of nectar which the gods churned out of the ocean. I keep it safely and give it to them when they need it. That is the reason our gods are immortal."

Narada told Megha that it was time to go home and helped her to climb down the tree. As she bid farewell

Rambha, the keeper of the Amrit Kalasha

to all the celestial beings that she had met in the sky, there were tears in her eyes. She slowly climbed back into her bed and as she slept, she dreamed about them. When she got up in the morning, the tree had disappeared but in the sky was a golden glow and she knew that is where all these beings lived. She folded her hands in reverence, and as she did so, there was a shower of flowers in her garden. Megha felt happy and knew that all these beings would always be with her.

॥ वृक्षः रक्षति रक्षितः ॥

Let us protect trees that protect us.